THE SECRET LIFE OF PETS 2: 2020
A CENTUM BOOK 978-1-913072-37-7
Published in Great Britain by Centum Books Ltd
This edition published 2019
1 3 5 7 9 10 8 6 4 2

 © 2019 Universal City Studios LLC. The Secret Life of Pets 2 is a trademark and copyright of Universal Studios. All Rights Reserved.

Centum Books Ltd, 20 Devon Square, Newton Abbot, Devon, TQ12 2HR, UK

books@centumbooksltd.co.uk

CENTUM BOOKS Limited Reg. No. 07641486

A CIP catalogue record for this book is available from the British Library.

Printed in Poland.

ILLUMINATION PRESENTS

THE SECRET LIFE OF PETS 2

THIS BOOK BELONGS TO:

CONTENTS

Max, Gidget, Snowball and all the Pets are ready for action. There are puzzles on Uncle Shep's farm, cat games galore – and a white tiger to be rescued! **The owners are away, so turn the page to find out what secrets are in store...**

LET'SGO

WHAT MISSING SOCKS?

Pickles from Pops' Puppy School has got his paws on **5 odd socks. Can you find them hidden on pages throughout the book?** Tick them below as you find them.

MEET THE PETS!

Get to know the old gang and some new friends on the block.

DUKE

Duke is Max's adopted brother and the enthusiastic answer to the question, "Who's a good boy?" He enjoys farm life and takes a far more relaxed approach towards the care of Liam, but he is always there for Max in his time of need.

MAX

Max lives the most pampered life imaginable. He's got a supportive brother in Duke, a loving owner in Katie and two new members of the family – Katie's husband, Chuck, and their baby boy Liam. Once wary of children, Max has come to adore Liam, following him around like a helicopter parent to make sure he is 100% safe at all times.

GIDGET

Gidget is a well-groomed but gutsy Pomeranian. When she accidentally knocks Max's favourite toy off the balcony into a cat lady's apartment, she has to learn from Chloe how to become a cat in order to infiltrate the cats' lair and get it back.

MEL

Mel is an excitable pug who struggles to stay focused when he's recruited by Max to be part of Liam's security detail. Even when he's supposed to be helping Snowball save Hu, he's got his own ulterior mission: *snacks*.

NORMAN

Norman the guinea pig is the most enthusiastic of the security team Max puts together to guard Liam. Unfortunately, Norman is the last Pet who should be in charge of any kind of 'intelligence'.

BUDDY

Buddy is a wiry, sarcastic dachshund who is part of Max's security team for Liam, watching the toddler's every move. He'll also suit up with Snowball to help rescue Hu, the tiger.

MEET THE PETS!

CHLOE

Chloe is a tabby cat with a passion for cake. She loves food, lying down and herself. Chloe lives above Max so she likes to visit him and, despite having a no-can-do attitude, she is always there for her friends.

SWEET PEA

This fearless budgie agrees to help Gidget learn the ways of the cat.

POPS

Pops is an old basset hound who tells it like it is. He has started a Puppy School, training pups to use their cuteness to get their own way.

DAISY

Daisy is an adorable shih tzu with an enormous personality who isn't afraid to speak her mind. She and her new friend Snowball band together to save Hu.

SNOWBALL

Snowball is a former leader of an animal gang, and now an official domesticated Pet. He likes to watch super hero TV shows with his owner, Molly. Molly has made him a super hero costume and he likes to spend his day practising super hero stuff.

ROOSTER

Rooster is Max's new friend – a farm dog full of country knowledge. He wears a bandana and saves Max from a turkey with just one bark. Maybe this confident dog can teach Max to be calm and not worry so much.

COLOUR DAISY AND ROOSTER AND HIS BANDANA!

FARM FRIGHTS!

Max is taken on a trip to Uncle Shep's farm, but this city dog doesn't know anything about country life! **Can you help him with these farmyard challenges?**

TURKEY RUN

Max is terrified of the turkey – especially when it's chasing after him! **Which line will help him avoid the fence and get safely into the field?**

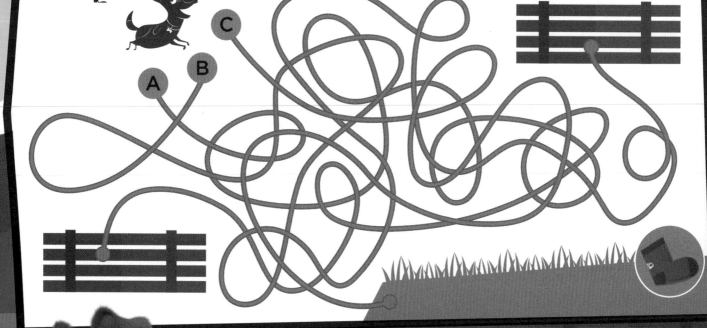

A B C

Fill in the missing letters to reveal some things Max sees on the farm.

Use these letters in the empty spaces:

A E I O

TR_CT_R   C_W

F_NC_   P_G

WH__T   L_MB

ANSWERS ON PAGE 51

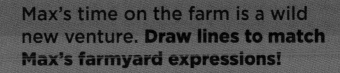

Max's time on the farm is a wild new venture. **Draw lines to match Max's farmyard expressions!**

COUNTING COWS

The farm is full of strange new animals that Max has never seen in the city. **Count the cows.**

Number of cows

GIDGET GAMES

While Max is on the farm, Gidget is at home with the other Pets having some **fun** of her own...

Who else is back at the apartment building with Gidget? **Match the Pets to the mystery shadows.**

1

A

2

B

3

C

4

D

Max leaves something precious behind with Gidget. **WHAT IS IT? Circle every third letter.**

START

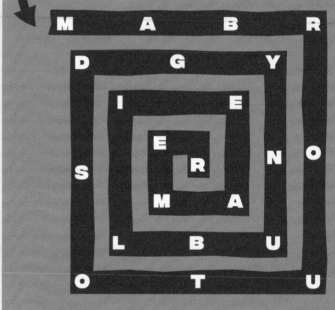

M A B R
D G Y
I E
E
S R N O
M A
L B U
O T U

Write your answer here:

____ ____ ____ ____

____ __ ____ ____

14   **ANSWERS ON PAGE 51**

GIDGET LOVES...

Gidget is spoiled by her loving owners. **What three things would she choose from these items?**

ANSWERS ON PAGE 51

SNOWBALL'S SEARCH

HELP SNOWBALL SAVE HU BY FINDING THE WORDS BELOW. CAN YOU FIND ALL THESE WORDS HIDDEN IN THE GRID? LOOK UP, DOWN, ACROSS AND DIAGONALLY.

						L	Y	R	U	P	H	A	T				
R	Y	U	A	L	M	O	L	F	M	U	R	T	T	T	U	O	
R	E	G	I	T	R	O	C	A	O	I	N	N	P	R	P		
B	H	G	S	F	P	O	H	C	O	F	I	C	M	S	B	E	
S	M	B	C	U	Y	H	Y	A	G	C	H	Y	E	P	E	P	
U	T	N	B	U	P	Y	I	S	E	T	U	P	M	O	W	G	
P	A	Y	C	I	S	E	H	R	E	T	U	N	F	U	S	R	B
E	U	F	F	H	C	E	R	G	N	N	B	T	Y	A	B		
R	L	N	P	T	U	G	R	P	N	N	B	P	M	S	F	A	Q
H	S	R	H	R	M	F	L	G	H	E	E	M	O	I	U	C	
E	Y	I	G	G	T	C	F	I	E	M	B	I	R	C	L	O	L
R	M	C	I	A	A	E	O	B	B	A	E	N	O	R	T	B	
O	B	H	I	R	P	Y	T	B	U	C	B	L	T	N	O	H	S
R	H	M	N	R	E	B	U	C	L	T	U	S	R	L	E	R	A
P	G	L	Y	S	C	L	C	A	P	U	H	U	L	B	Y	L	G
C	F	T	G	O	F	U	P	S	Y	Y	N	B	S	N	R		
A	G	S	L	C	A	P	S										

Word List

MOLLY

SUPER HERO

COSTUME

HU

TIGER

CIRCUS

SERGEI

SNOWBALL'S NEW FRIEND IS HIDING IN THE GRID, TOO. CAN YOU FIND HER?

16

ANSWERS ON PAGE 51

DESIGN A COSTUME

SNOWBALL'S AMAZING SUPER HERO COSTUME TRANSFORMS HIM INTO...
CAPTAIN SNOWBALL! DESIGN YOUR OWN COSTUME FOR SNOWBALL
IN ANY STYLE.

COSTUME STYLE: _____

SPECIAL FEATURES: _____

SNOWBALL'S NEW NICKNAME: _____

PET SCRAMBLES

The Pets are all running around the city on separate missions and they can't find each other. **Unscramble the names to get them back together – QUICK!**

G E T D I G

_ _ _ _ _ _ _

U B D Y D

_ _ _ _ _

L A W B L O N S

_ _ _ _ _ _ _ _ _

A X M

_ _ _

Y A I S D

_ _ _ _ _

K U D E

_ _ _ _

E L O C H

_ _ _ _ _

ANSWERS ON PAGE 51

MAX'S CODE

Max is worried and sends out a message to all the Pets with his walkie-talkie system. **What is the message? Crack the code to find out.**

A	B	C	D	E	F	G	H	I	J	K	L	M
1	2	3	4	5	6	7	8	9	10	11	12	13

N	O	P	Q	R	S	T	U	V	W	X	Y	Z
14	15	16	17	18	19	20	21	22	23	24	25	26

2	1	2	25

12	9	1	13

9	19

13	9	19	19	9	14	7!

Colour Max once you have solved the code.

YOU CAN USE THE SAME CODE TO SEND A SECRET MESSAGE TO A FRIEND!

ANSWERS ON PAGE 51

POPS' PUPPY SCHOOL

The puppy Pets are learning to get away with anything – just by using their extreme levels of cuteness! **Help them with their lessons in Puppy School.**

Practise being as adorable as Pickles!
Copy this picture of him so he's ready for his lessons. You can use the grid lines as a guide.

ANSWERS ON PAGE 51

Who else is in class with Pickles?
Complete the names.

| P | | IN | | E | SS |

| | T | | | Y | |

| | M | | M | | |

| GE | | | R | G | |

George attends Puppy School even though he's a kitten! **Can you find his toy mouse?** It's a little different from all the others.

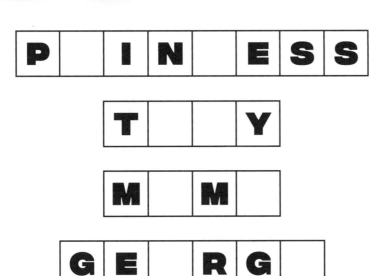

ANSWERS ON PAGE 51

CATNAPS WITH CHLOE

Chloe was ready to lie down, but she's had a little too much catnip! **Help her unpick these puzzles** so she can get her fifth nap of the day.

1 HOW TO CAT

Gidget needs Chloe's tips on how to act like a cat. **Can you find Chloe in the picture** so she can share her cat tips?

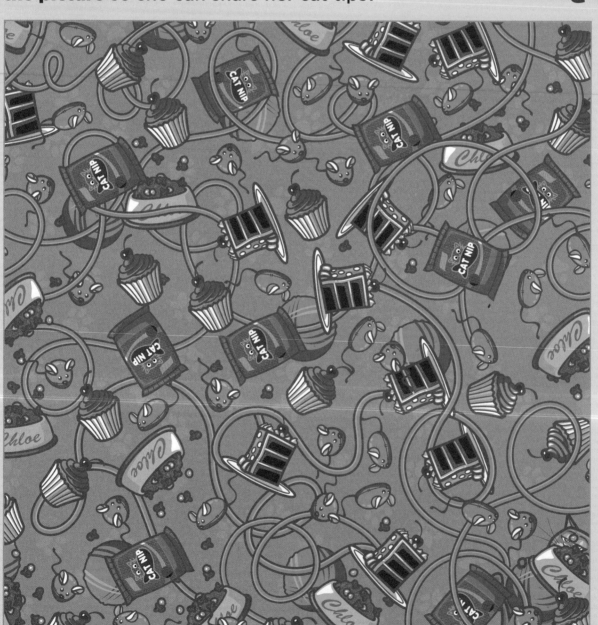

ANSWERS ON PAGE 52

2 TANGLED WOOL

Chloe is looking for her toy mouse. **Which wool line will reel him back in?**

3 CURRENT MOOD

Chloe can't be bothered with all these energetic games. **Which face is an exact match for her expression?**

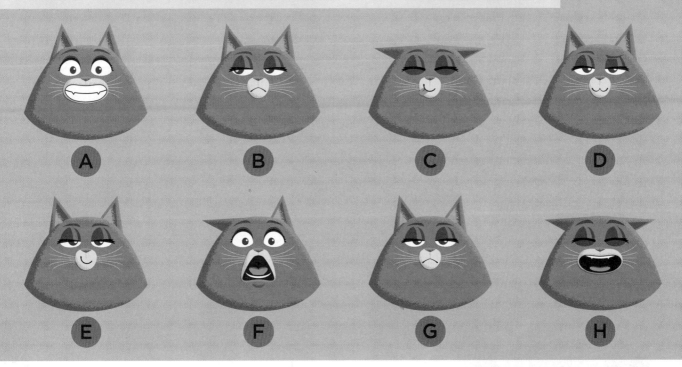

BUSY BEE RESCUE

This is it – Gidget is going into the cat lady's apartment to rescue Busy Bee! **Help her through the maze to pick up Busy Bee**, and **then escape to the finish**. Make sure she **avoids** the **clever cats** along the way!

START

ANSWERS ON PAGE 52

FINISH

CHLOE IS HELPING GIDGET — CAN YOU SPOT HER IN THE MAZE?

FARMYARD PATTERNS

With some help from Rooster, Max is actually starting to enjoy farm life. **Can you work out which picture comes next in each line? Write the correct letter in each box.**

A   **B**   **C**   **D**

1

2

3

4

5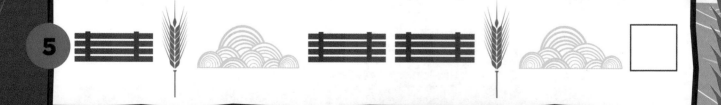

ANSWERS ON PAGE 52

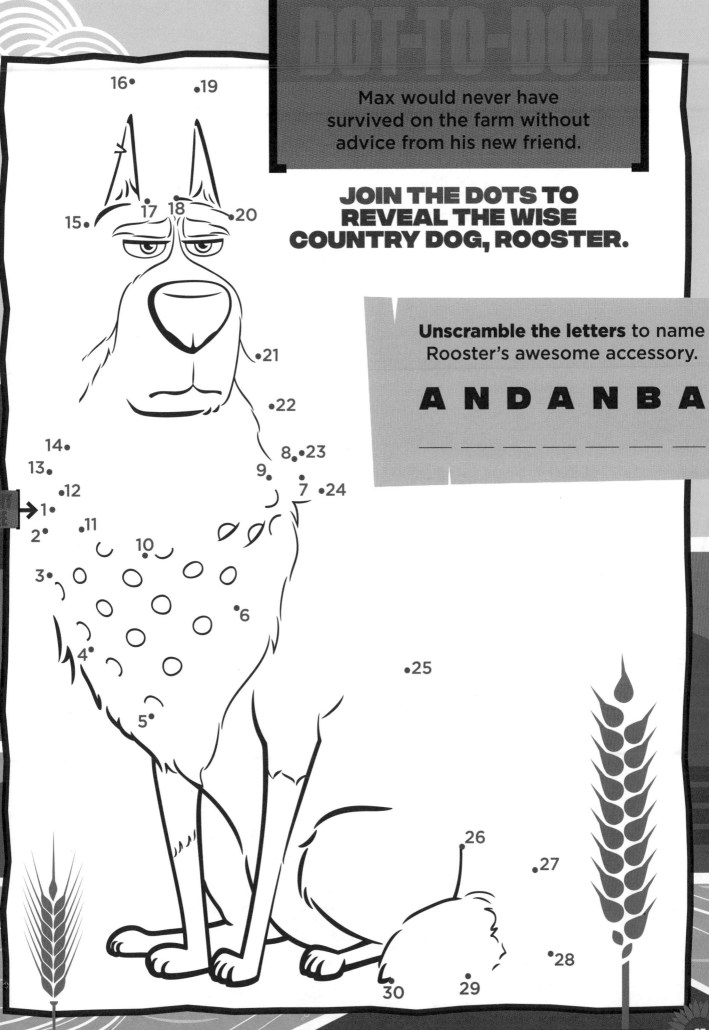

DOT-TO-DOT

Max would never have survived on the farm without advice from his new friend.

JOIN THE DOTS TO REVEAL THE WISE COUNTRY DOG, ROOSTER.

Unscramble the letters to name Rooster's awesome accessory.

A N D A N B A

_ _ _ _ _ _ _

START HERE

SUPER HERO PUZZLES

THE BUCKTOOTH PET IS FINDING HIS INNER HERO.
HELP SNOWBALL SUIT UP AND FACE THESE PUZZLES LIKE A CHAMP!

A WHAT IS THE NAME OF THE SUPER HERO CLOAK WORN AROUND THE NECK?

B WHO IS SNOWBALL'S NEW SHIH TZU FRIEND?

C WHICH DOG HAS A PUPPY SCHOOL IN HIS APARTMENT?

D SNOWBALL WANTS TO RESCUE HU – WHAT KIND OF ANIMAL IS HU? A WHITE

E WHAT'S THE NAME OF THE TERRIER WHO LIVES NEAR SNOWBALL?

F WHO IS THE EVIL CIRCUS OWNER WHO HAS TRAPPED HU?

G WHO IS MOLLY? SHE IS SNOWBALL'S

SNOWBALL

ANSWERS ON PAGE 52

THE REAL SNOWBALL

WHICH SNOWBALL IS THE REAL DEAL? FIND THE ODD SNOWBALL OUT, AND THAT'S OUR HERO.

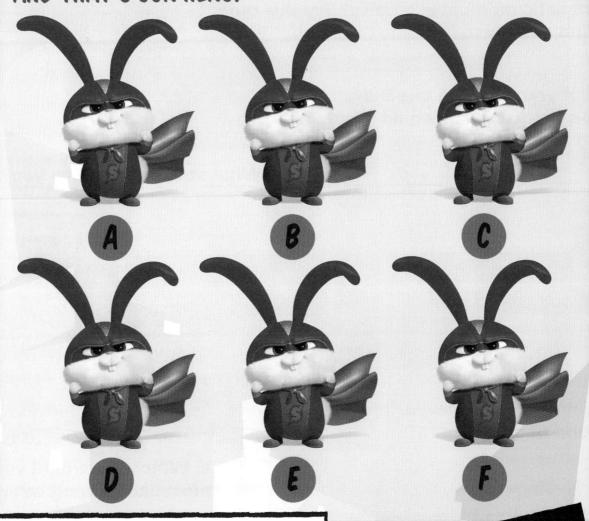

A   B   C

D   E   F

MOLLY AND SNOWBALL WERE INSPIRED BY SUPER HERO TV SHOWS. WHAT WOULD A SNOWBALL SHOW LOOK LIKE? DOODLE A SCENE ON THIS TV SCREEN.

SNOWBALL FOREVER

LIST THREE WORDS THAT YOU THINK BEST DESCRIBE SNOWBALL!

PET PERSONALITY

Are you super loyal like Max, or do you love a dramatic moment like Daisy? **Try this quiz to find out which Pet is just like you.**

1. If you could do one thing on this list, what would it be?

A Play outside all day

B Go on holiday

C Play video games

D Watch TV with friends

2. What sounds most like you?

A Excitable and loyal

B Brave and dramatic

C imaginative and funny

D Friendly and talented

3. What's your favourite kind of animal?

A Dog

B Tiger

C Rabbit

D Cat

4. Which Pet would you most like to hang out with?

A Rooster

B Snowball

C Daisy

D Chloe

5. If you had to wear one of these for a whole day, what would you pick?

A A bandana

B A pink bow

C A fancy-dress costume

D A tiara

6. What would be the best day trip?

A To a farm in the countryside

B Shopping in a big city

C To a theme park

D To a swimming pool

7. What kind of video game would you like best?

A A puzzle game

B A treasure hunt

C A super hero game

D A building game

NOW COUNT UP YOUR **ANSWERS** TO FIND YOUR PET TWIN!

Mostly A's
MAX
You've got loads of energy and everyone knows you're a loyal friend. You won't let fear hold you back.

Mostly B's
DAISY
You're great at telling stories. You always remember to look out for friends.

Mostly C's
SNOWBALL
There's no end to your wild imagination! You're creative and fun, and you'll always achieve what you set out to do.

Mostly D's
GIDGET
You're smart and committed in everything you do. If there is a friend in need, you'll be the first one to help.

COLOUR THE PET THAT IS JUST LIKE YOU.

31

A HOWLIN' GOOD TIME

What does a real country dog do? He climbs up on a truck and howls at the moon! **Colour** the new friends, **Rooster and Max.**

There's a lot of work to be done on the farm. **Help Rooster get these items in order by filling in the sum totals.**

1

= ☐

2

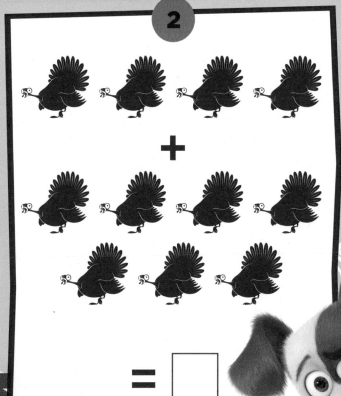

= ☐

3

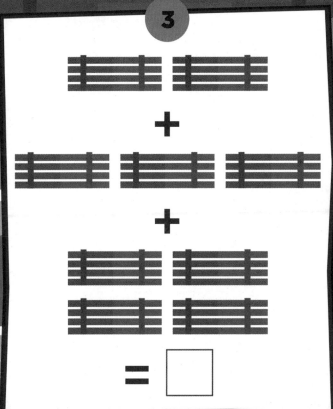

= ☐

4

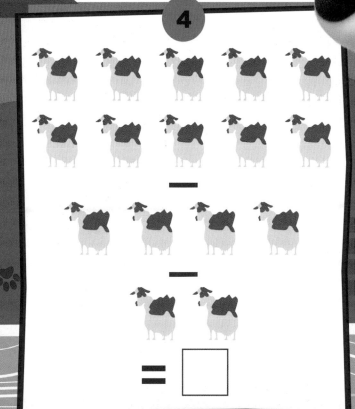

= ☐

How many muddy paw prints appear on the page? ☐

ANSWERS ON PAGE 52

DESIGN A TAG

Max is so proud of his name tag from Katie – it shows he's a proper Pet!

DESIGN A FANCY NEW NAME TAG FOR MAX.

Write Max's name on the tag and colour it in!

34

The Pets live in an apartment building, so it's easy for them to visit each other on different floors. **In the game below, can you move down the floors from WALK to TAIL using the clues as a guide?**

HINT: Only one letter changes on each floor.

W A L K

1 A barrier made of bricks.

2 A round toy that the Pets love to play with.

3 This happens when you trip over or lose balance.

4 If you don't succeed at something.

5 A little metal object that is hit with a hammer.

T A I L

ANSWERS ON PAGE 52

LEND A PAW

Pop into the Puppy School and **help Pickles solve this word game**. Each answer begins with a letter in his name.

1. Which old dog hosts the Puppy School? **P** ☐ ☐ ☐

2. What is the opposite of outside? **I** ☐ ☐ ▓ ☐ ☐

3. What kind of animal is Chloe? **C** ☐ ▓

4. What is the name of Max's owner? **K** ☐ ☐ ☐ ☐

5. What do the pups do at School? **L** ☐ ☐ ☐ ☐ ▓

6. What is the opposite of difficult? **E** ☐ ☐ ▓

7. What does Snowball dress up as? **S** ☐ ☐ ☐
☐ ☐ ☐ ☐

One of the cute students has been up to mischief! **Unscramble the highlighted letters** to find out who it was.

▓ ▓ ▓ ▓

Circle the mischievous Pet!

PRINCESS DIFFERENCES

Princess is catching up on her Puppy School reading.
Can you spot 6 differences in the second picture?

Colour a bone for every difference you spot.

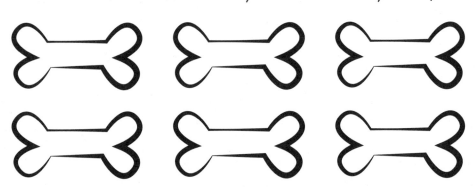

ANSWERS ON PAGE 52

PET RUMOURS

There are some strange stories floating around the Pets' apartment building. **Can you work out which are likely to be true and which are false?**

TRUE FALSE

1 MAX HAS A NEW BANDANA-WEARING FARM FRIEND.

2 NORMAN IS ON A TRIP TO THE COUNTRY WITH MAX.

3 CHLOE HAS DRESSED UP AS A DOG.

4 SNOWBALL IS WEARING A SUPER HERO COSTUME AND PRETENDING TO FLY.

5 A DALMATIAN CALLED PRINCESS HAS ASKED FOR SNOWBALL'S HELP.

6 NORMAN IS USING A LASER POINTER TO DISTRACT A BUNCH OF CATS.

7 A HUGE WHITE TIGER HAS BEEN SPOTTED IN POPS' APARTMENT.

8 A CIRCUS OWNER CALLED SERGEI WANTS TO PLAY BALL WITH THE PETS.

9 DAISY IS BEING CHASED BY A PACK OF CIRCUS WOLVES.

10 MAX HAS DECIDED TO JOIN THE CIRCUS.

38 ANSWERS ON PAGE 52

DUKE'S DICE GAME

Duke is a big, furry ball of fun! Take him on a city adventure and **use a dice to colour him in.**

CHOOSE AN AREA TO COLOUR, THEN **ROLL YOUR DICE** AND USE THE KEY TO FIND WHAT COLOUR TO USE!

COLOUR KEY

1 Brown
2 Blue
3 Pink

4 Grey
5 Yellow
6 Green

WRITE A PETS STORY

WOULD YOU LIKE TO CREATE YOUR OWN STORY FOR THE PETS? NOW YOU CAN!

FILL IN YOUR ANSWERS ON THIS PAGE AND THEN FOLLOW THE INSTRUCTIONS ON PAGE 41.

1 WHICH PET IS YOUR FAVOURITE?

2 WHAT'S YOUR FAVOURITE COLOUR?

3 WHAT IS YOUR FAVOURITE TOY?

4 WHAT PET MAKES YOU LAUGH THE MOST?

5 NAME SOMETHING THAT HOLDS WATER.

6 WHICH PET IS THE CUTEST?

7 NAME YOUR FAVOURITE FANCY-DRESS COSTUME.

8 HOW DO YOU FEEL WHEN YOU'RE TRYING SOMETHING NEW?

9 WHAT'S YOUR FAVOURITE TYPE OF ANIMAL?

10 WHAT'S YOUR FAVOURITE PLACE TO GO AT THE WEEKEND?

11 WHAT TIME IS IT JUST NOW?

12 NAME A GOOD FEELING.

ALL OF THE PETS WERE SURPRISED WHEN [1] _____ TOLD THEM THEY WERE GOING ON A VISIT TO A FARM. [1] _____ DIDN'T KNOW ANYTHING ABOUT THE COUNTRY AND DIDN'T LIKE MUD! IT MADE THEIR [2] _____ FUR DIRTY AND STICKY.

WHILE [1] _____ WAS AWAY, THEY LEFT THEIR [3] _____ WITH [4] _____ . THIS PET WAS TO LOOK AFTER IT CAREFULLY. UNFORTUNATELY [4] _____ FELL ASLEEP AND DROPPED THE [3] _____ INTO A [5] _____ .

MEANWHILE [6] _____ GOT A NEW COSTUME FROM THEIR OWNER. IT WAS A [7] _____ COSTUME. [6] _____ WAS VERY [8] _____ .

[6] _____ WAS TOLD THAT A [9] _____ NEEDED RESCUING, SO THEY PUT ON THEIR [7] _____ COSTUME AND RUSHED TO THE [10] _____ . WHEN [1] _____ AND [4] _____ HEARD, THEY RUSHED TO HELP. TOGETHER, THEY SAVED THE [9] _____ .

THE PETS ALL RUSHED TO BE HOME BY [11] _____ WHEN THEY HAD TO BE IN BED. THEIR OWNERS WERE ALL VERY [12] _____ .

TRY CHANGING YOUR ANSWERS ON PAGE 40 AND SEE WHAT HAPPENS TO YOUR STORY!

WHEN YOU ARE FINISHED, READ YOUR STORY ALOUD!

41

GIDGET JIGSAW

Let the fluff fly! Gidget's fur is all tangled up. Can you brush her back together by **putting the missing pieces in place?**

ANSWERS ON PAGE 53

SPOT THE CATS

Gidget is getting quite used to being surrounded by cats! **How many times can you spot the word CAT in the grid?**

LOOK ACROSS, UP, DOWN AND DIAGONALLY.

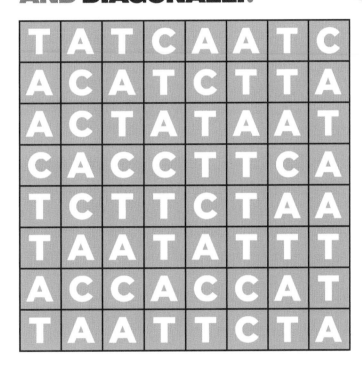

T	A	T	C	A	A	T	C
A	C	A	T	C	T	T	A
A	C	T	A	T	A	A	T
C	A	C	C	T	T	C	A
T	C	T	T	C	T	A	A
T	A	A	T	A	T	T	T
A	C	C	A	C	C	A	T
T	A	A	T	T	C	T	A

SECRET LIFE OF PETS

How many **new words** can you make from the letters above? For example:

POT _____ _____

STEP _____ _____

FLIP _____ _____

ANSWERS ON PAGE 53

WOULD YOU RATHER...

Play this game with Gidget and
tick just one option for every question!

WHAT WOULD YOU RATHER DO...

BE A DOG **OR** BE A CAT?

☑ ☑

VISIT THE FARM WITH MAX

OR

HANG OUT IN THE CITY
WITH SNOWBALL?

CLEAN OUT CHLOE'S
CAT LITTER

☑

OR

TAKE MEL FOR A WALK?

☑

HAVE NORMAN AS A PET

☑

OR

HAVE SWEET PEA AS A PET?

☑

CREATE A COSTUME
FOR GIDGET

☑

OR

DESIGN A COSTUME
FOR SNOWBALL?

☑

GET A HUG FROM HU

☑

OR

PLAY IN THE MUD
WITH ROOSTER?

☑

HAVE DAISY AS A PET

☑

OR

HAVE CHLOE AS A PET?

☑

BE ABLE TO TALK TO
ANIMALS FOR A WEEK

☑

OR

BECOME AN ANIMAL
FOR ONE DAY?

☑

SAY CAKE!

Chloe has had her fill of fridge treats today, so she's very happy.
Complete this satisfied cat by drawing the other half of her face.

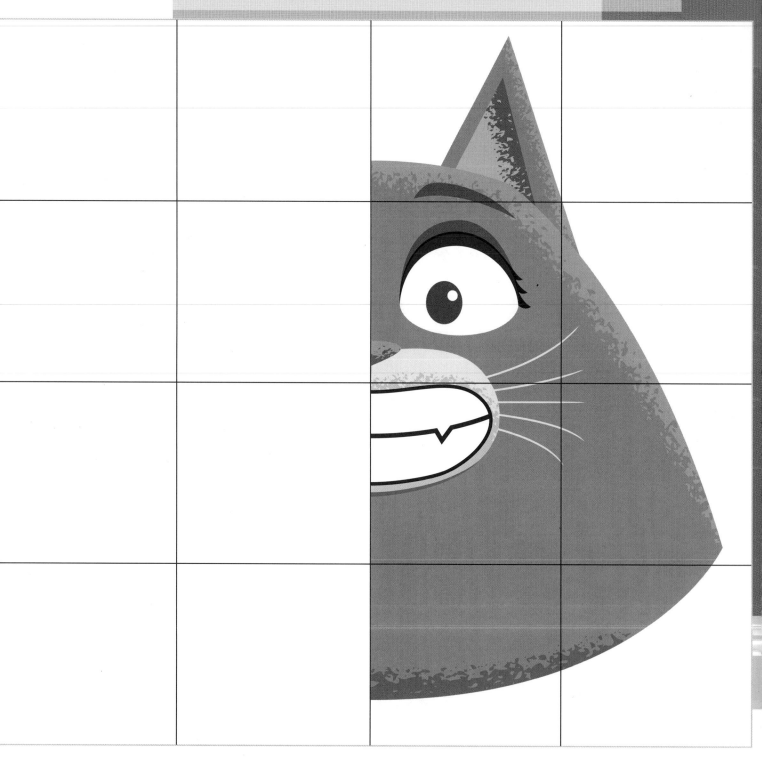

NOW COLOUR THE COMPLETED CHLOE SO YOUR DRAWING MATCHES THE OTHER HALF.

Chloe

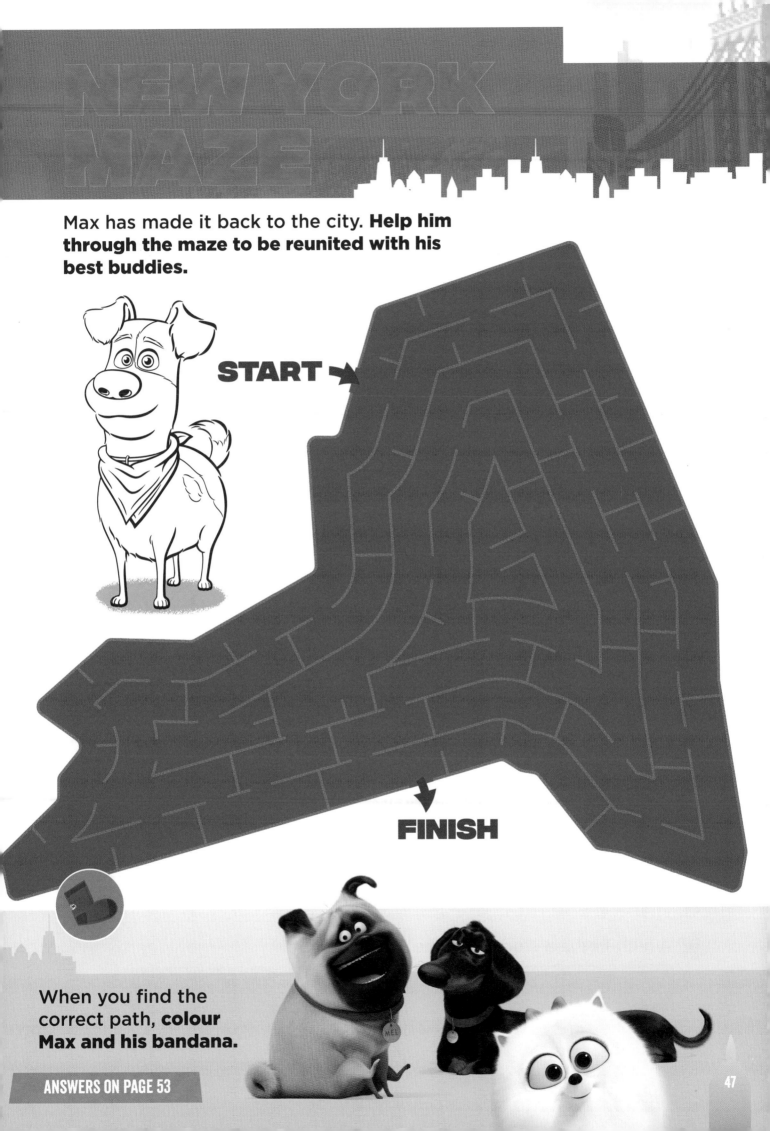

Max has made it back to the city. **Help him through the maze to be reunited with his best buddies.**

START →

↓
FINISH

When you find the correct path, **colour Max and his bandana.**

SECRET LIFE OF PETS 2 QUIZ!

How well do you know Max, Snowball and the rest of the gang? See how far you can get with these **trivia questions.**

EASY

TRY THESE TO GET YOUR PAWS WARMED UP!

1 What colour is Gidget?

2 Which big dog lives with Max?

A BUDDY   B DUKE   C SWEET PEA

3 Which dog runs the Puppy School?

4 Who helps Gidget train as a cat?

A DAISY   B MAX   C CHLOE

5 What is the name of Katie's baby?

6 What does Snowball like to play?

A VIDEO GAMES   B CARD GAMES   C HIDE-AND-SEEK

7 Which toy does Gidget look after for Max?

8 Which Pet is a student at the Puppy School?

A NORMAN   B PRINCESS   C CHLOE

ANSWERS ON PAGE 53

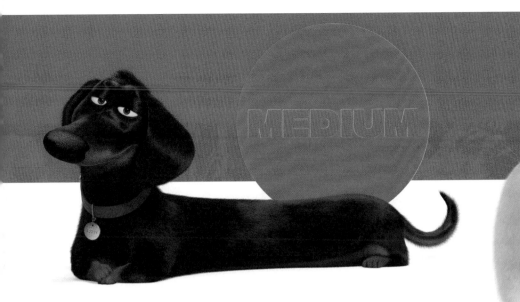

THESE QUESTIONS ARE A LITTLE TRICKIER – HOW FAR CAN YOU GET?

1 Which pet belongs to Molly?

A MAX   B POPS   C SNOWBALL

2 What breed of dog is Max?

3 Whose safety is Max's security team looking out for?

4 What is Hu guarded by in the zoo?

A ELEPHANTS   B TIGERS   C WOLVES

5 What animal does Gidget disguise herself as?

6 What kind of animal is Norman?

A BUDGIE   B GUINEA PIG   C DOG

7 What animal chases Max on the farm?

8 What's the name of Max's new farm friend?

A ROOSTER   B COTTON   C SHEP

IF YOU CAN ANSWER THESE QUESTIONS, YOU ARE A PETS SUPERFAN!

1 What breed of dog is Daisy?

| A SHIH TZU | B TERRIER | C POODLE |

2 What bedtime story does Max read to baby Liam?

| A THE THREE LITTLE PIGS | B LITTLE RED RIDING HOOD | C GOLDILOCKS AND THE THREE BEARS |

3 Who owns the farm that Max goes to visit?

4 What's the name of circus owner who keeps Hu locked up?

5 Who helps Gidget by using a laser pointer?

| A CHLOE | B MAX | C NORMAN |

6 What is Snowball's super hero name?

7 Which of these is not the name of a Puppy School Pet?

| A GEORGE | B MIMI | C ARTHUR |

8 What does Chloe wear on her head when she has too much catnip?

| A A LAMPSHADE | B A BOWL | C A WOOLLY HAT |

ANSWERS

PAGE 7

The odd socks are on pages
11
12
20
29
47

PAGES 12-13

Line C

TRACTOR   COW

FENCE   PIG

WHEAT   LAMB

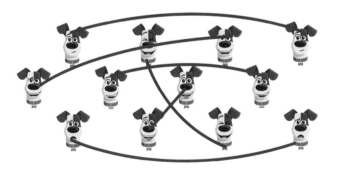

13 cows

PAGES 14-15

1. 1-B, 2-C, 3-D, 4-A, 2. Busy Bee,
3. Perfume, tiara and brush

PAGE 16

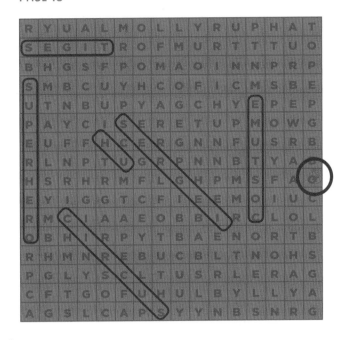

PAGE 18

GIDGET, BUDDY, SNOWBALL,
MAX, DAISY, DUKE, CHLOE

PAGE 19

BABY LIAM IS MISSING!

PAGES 20-21

PRINCESS

TINY

MIMI

GEORGE

ANSWERS

PAGES 22-23

1.

2. C

3. G

PAGES 24-25

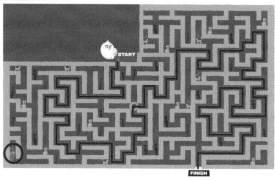

PAGE 26

1. C, 2. A, 3. D, 4. C, 5. B

PAGE 27

Bandana

PAGES 28-29

A – Cape, B – Daisy,
C – Pops, D – Tiger, E – Max,
F – Sergei, G – Owner
Captain Snowball
THE REAL SNOWBALL: D

PAGE 33

1. 8, 2. 11, 3. 9, 4. 4
10 muddy paw prints.

PAGE 35

1. Wall,
2. Ball,
3. Fall,
4. Fail,
5. Nail

PAGE 36

1. Pops, 2. Inside, 3. Cat,
4. Katie, 5. Learn, 6. Easy,
7. Super hero

PAGE 37

PAGE 38

1. True, 2. False, 3. False, 4. True,
5. False, 6. True, 7. True, 8. False,
9. True, 10. False

PAGE 42
1. F, 2. A, 3. E, 4. B, 5. C, 6. D

PAGE 43

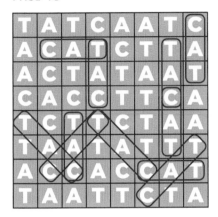

PAGE 47

PAGES 48-50
EASY: 1. White, 2. B, 3. Pops,
4. C, 5. Liam, 6. A, 7. Busy Bee,
8. B
MEDIUM: 1. C, 2. Terrier,
3. Baby Liam, 4. C, 5. Cat, 6. B,
7. Turkey, 8. A
HARD: 1. A, 2. B, 3. Uncle Shep,
4. Sergei, 5. C, 6. Captain
Snowball, 7. C, 8. A